TINKLE
WHERE LEARNING MEETS FUN

BUTTERFINGERS COLLECTION

Log on to: www.tinkleonline.com

DIWALI WITH BUTTERFINGERS

Story: Khyrunnisa A.
Script: Janaki Viswanathan
Illustrations: Abhijeet Kini

IT'S GOING TO BE A CRACKER OF A DIWALI!

NO, BUTTERFINGERS! THIS IS GOING TO BE A DAZZLER OF A DIWALI!

AMAR WAS CALLED BUTTERFINGERS BECAUSE HE HAD A HABIT OF DROPPING THINGS.

DAZZLER? WHAT DO YOU MEAN, KIRAN?

MEANING, THE WHOLE PLACE WILL BE DAZZLED BY THE LIGHT OF SPARKLERS, CATHERINE WHEELS, FLOWER SHOWERS…

…AND ROCKETS!

I HAVE AN IDEA! HOW ABOUT GETTING THE ROCKETS BUT LETTING THEM OFF WHEN THE GROWN-UPS AREN'T WITH US?

HOLD ON A SECOND, WHY ARE THE GROWN-UPS GOING TO BE WITH US IN THE FIRST PLACE??

ROCKETS? NO SUCH LUCK. MY DAD'S REFUSED TO BUY ME ANY.

OH, BUT WHY, ERIC?

MY DAD TOO. HE SAYS THEY'RE DANGEROUS!

WELL, I WAS JUST THINKING…HOW ABOUT WE GET THE GROWN-UPS TO JOIN US FOR THAT DIWALI PARTY WE'RE PLANNING? TO SORT OF TAKE THEM BACK TO THEIR CHILDHOOD DAYS OF FUN!

IN OTHER WORDS, THE DAYS WHEN THEY WERE HUMAN, EH?

BUT WHEN AND WHERE DO WE HAVE THIS PARTY?

TWO DAYS BEFORE DIWALI? AS FOR WHERE…

…WHY, YOUR BACKYARD OF COURSE, BUTTERFINGERS! IT'S THE BIGGEST ONE IN THE NEIGHBOURHOOD.

OVER THE NEXT WEEK—

YOU WANT US TO COME FOR YOUR DIWALI PARTY?

YES, MA. WE THOUGHT IT WOULD BE FUN.

I'D LIKE THAT!

LATER —

I SAY, MY PARENTS WERE REALLY TOUCHED THAT WE INVITED THEM TO OUR PARTY.

THAT EXPLAINS TEN BOXES OF FLOWER SHOWERS, EH? HEH HEH!

HERE, ANOTHER BOX OF CATHERINE WHEELS. WE HAVE A NICE STOCK FOR OUR PARTY NOW!

WHAT ABOUT THE ROCKETS?

RIGHT AT THE BACK WHERE NOBODY CAN SEE THEM! WE'LL LET THEM OUT ONE OF THESE DAYS, BEFORE OR AFTER THE GROWN-UP PARTY.

BUT TWO DAYS LATER—

THE PARTY'S CANCELLED? BUT WHY? HOW?

MY DAD'S GONE INTO ONE OF HIS MOODS AGAIN. YOU KNOW WHAT I'M TALKING ABOUT, KIRAN!

THE WORLD-IS-SO-SAD-HOW-DARE-YOU-CELEBRATE, MOOD, EH?

YEP! HE GAVE ME A TWO-HOUR LECTURE ON HOW SELFISH WE WERE TO HAVE A PARTY WHEN SHYAMU AND HIS PARENTS CAN BARELY AFFORD TWO SQUARE MEALS A DAY.

SHYAMU WAS A FRIEND OF THE BOYS AND LIVED NEXT TO AMAR'S HOUSE. HIS PARENTS WERE DAY LABOURERS.

SO? WE'LL CALL SHYAMU FOR THE PARTY AS WELL.

HIS FATHER WON'T LET HIM COME. DON'T YOU KNOW THEIR STORY?

3

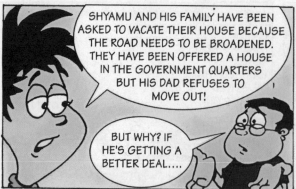

SHYAMU AND HIS FAMILY HAVE BEEN ASKED TO VACATE THEIR HOUSE BECAUSE THE ROAD NEEDS TO BE BROADENED. THEY HAVE BEEN OFFERED A HOUSE IN THE GOVERNMENT QUARTERS BUT HIS DAD REFUSES TO MOVE OUT!

BUT WHY? IF HE'S GETTING A BETTER DEAL....

WELL, HE'S IN ONE OF HIS MOODS!

PARENTS AND THEIR MOODS!

SO NO PARTY ...NO ROCKETS?

ACTUALLY, I DO HAVE ANOTHER IDEA!

MY PARENTS ARE GOING OUT TODAY EVENING. THEY'LL RETURN LATE. HOW ABOUT WE HAVE A QUICK AND QUIET PARTY WHILE THEY'RE GONE??

HMMM... THAT'S A THOUGHT!

YOU THREE COME BACK HERE AT 7:30 P.M. I NEED SOME TIME TO ORGANIZE STUFF.

TO DROP STUFF, YOU MEAN, BUTTERFINGERS!

YOU KNOW HE HASN'T DROPPED ANYTHING FOR THE PAST WEEK?! ANY LONGER AND WE'LL BE FORCED TO CALL HIM BY HIS REAL NAME!

OH, OH!

CRASH

I TAKE THAT BACK!

YOU WILL REMAIN 'BUTTERFINGERS' FOR ALL ETERNITY!

SUDDENLY—

HELP! FIRE!

HEY, THAT'S SHYAMU'S VOICE!

SO MANY ROCKETS CAME OUT OF NOWHERE LIKE ARROWS!

LOOK AT OUR HUT! IT'S BURNED DOWN!

UH OH! YOUR FOLKS ARE BACK, BUTTERFINGERS. WE'D BETTER GET GOING.

GULP!

WHAT ON EARTH HAPPENED TO SHYAMU'S HUT? WAS THERE AN ACCIDENT?

SHOULD I TELL HIM THE TRUTH...?

THE NEXT MORNING —

I WONDER IF BUTTERFINGERS HAS TOLD HIS DAD THAT IT WAS OUR ROCKETS THAT BURNED DOWN SHYAMU'S HUT.

WELL, WE'LL HAVE TO. POOR SHYAMU, I WONDER HOW HIS FAMILY'S MANAGING!

AH, THE CRACKER-PARTY-BOYS!

HE KNOWS!

WE'RE SORRY, MR KUMAR. THE ROCKETS....

THEY BURNED DOWN SHYAMU'S HUT. AND YOU HAD YOUR CRACKER PARTY DESPITE MY FORBIDDING IT. AMAR TOLD ME ALL ABOUT IT.

BUT YOU KNOW WHAT? I'M GLAD YOU DID! YOU MANAGED TO ACHIEVE WHAT THE PWD* COULDN'T!

HUH?

SHYAMU'S FATHER WAS FORCED TO MOVE TO THE GOVERNMENT QUARTERS BECAUSE HIS HUT BURNED DOWN. THEIR NEW HOUSE IS BIGGER AND CLEANER. AND THE PWD CAN FINALLY START WORK ON EXPANDING THE ROAD!

OH!

ALL THANKS TO OUR ROCKETS!

NOPE! ALL THANKS TO BUTTERFINGERS AND HIS SLIP-GRIP!

THAT'S RIGHT! AND BY THE WAY, I GUESS I WAS A LITTLE HARSH ON YOU BOYS. LET'S HAVE YOUR PARTY AGAIN, PROPERLY THIS TIME. HOW ABOUT TONIGHT?

AND THAT EVENING, THE PRE-DIWALI GROWN-UP PARTY WAS FINALLY HELD.

WHY ARE YOU HOLDING ON SO TIGHTLY TO THAT SPARKLER, BUTTERFINGERS?

WELL, I DON'T WANT ANY MORE SLIP-UPS! LET'S ALL HAVE A HAPPY AND SAFE DIWALI!

Butterfingers and the Centipede

Story: Khyrunnisa A.
Script: Anomita Guha
Illustrations: Abhijeet Kini

I WISH IT'D STOP RAINING...THE PLAYGROUND LOOKS LIKE A SWIMMING POOL!

UGH...WITH HUNDREDS OF CREEPY CRAWLIES DOING THE BACK STROKE IN IT!

CREEPY CRAWLIES! THAT REMINDS ME...I'VE GOT SOMETHING TO SHOW YOU!

HEY, GUYS! WET TODAY, ISN'T IT?

BUTTERFINGERS! I'VE ALREADY HAD A BATH IN THE MORNING!

STOP DROWNING ERIC, BUTTERFINGERS! HERE, CATCH THIS!

YIPES!

SQUISH!

OW!

UGH! IT'S A CENTIPEDE!

IDIOT! IT'S NOT REAL!

WHAT A BEAUTIFUL PLASTIC SPECIMEN!

IT'S MADE OF RUBBER, ACTUALLY....

BEAUTIFUL?! UGH! IF IT LANDED ON YOUR NOSE, YOU WOULDN'T SAY SO!

9

SOME TIME LATER —

AMAR, BRING YOUR BOOK UP HERE.

NOW'S MY CHANCE!

HERE, SIR...I...MY BOOK!

MUST YOU BE SO CARELESS?!

CRASH

OWW!

GASP! A GIANT CENTIPEDE!

UH-OH!

CAREFUL, BOYS! BACK AWAY! LET ME TAKE CARE OF THIS CREATURE!

THUMP!

IT'S STILL IN ONE PIECE! HOW STRANGE!

A FAKE CENTIPEDE! HOW DARE YOU BOYS PLAY A TRICK ON ME? WHOSE IS IT?

GULP...IT'S MINE, SIR! BUT WE DIDN'T MEAN TO....

ENOUGH! I WANT YOU TO WRITE 'I WILL NOT BRING A PLASTIC CENTIPEDE TO CLASS' 500 TIMES!

B...BUT...IT'S MADE OF RUBBER, SIR!

I DON'T CARE IF IT'S MADE OF GOLD! I'LL KEEP THE ABOMINABLE IMITATION ARTHROPOD PHYLUM OBJECT WITH ME!

T...THE... WHAT?

THE CENTIPEDE! AND KIRAN, I ALSO WANT YOUR PUNISHMENT SIGNED BY YOUR FATHER!

I'M DEAD!

DURING LUNCH BREAK —

I'LL HELP YOU WRITE OUT YOUR LINES!

BUT WHAT ABOUT MY DAD? HE'LL GO THROUGH THE ROOF WHEN HE SEES MY PUNISHMENT!

I WISH WE COULD PUT SIR IN A GOOD MOOD SOMEHOW.

AFTER HIS EXPERIENCES WITH CREEPY, WE'LL NEED A MIRACLE FOR THAT TO HAPPEN!

SORRY I PUSHED YOU, SIR, BUT THIS ONE WAS REAL!

THANK YOU, AMAR. YOU SAVED ME FROM A PAINFUL BITE!

SIR, THE FAKE CENTIPEDE...I DROPPED IT BY MISTAKE! IT REALLY WASN'T KIRAN'S FAULT.

HMM... WELL, HE SHOULDN'T HAVE BROUGHT IT TO SCHOOL SO THE PUNISHMENT STILL STANDS.

BUT...YOU DON'T HAVE TO GET IT SIGNED BY YOUR FATHER, KIRAN.

THANKS, SIR!

AND COULD HE PLEASE HAVE CREEPY...UH, I MEAN THE CENTIPEDE... BACK?

ONLY IF HE NEVER BRINGS IT TO SCHOOL AGAIN!

GULP! IT'S NOT HERE...I MUST HAVE DROPPED IT SOMEWHERE!

OH NO! HE'S AS BAD AS YOU, BUTTERFINGERS!

SCREAM

HEH HEH...I THINK IT'S BEEN FOUND, SIR!

WHEW!

Butterfingers and the Butterflies

Story: Khyrunnisa A.
Script: Anomita Guha
Illustrations: Abhijeet Kini

KIRAN AND AMAR (ALSO KNOWN AS BUTTERFINGERS) HAD ALARMING NEWS TO REPORT TO THEIR FRIENDS —

TRAGEDY! CHAOS!

CALAMITY HAS STRUCK!

WHAT ARE YOU BLABBERING ABOUT?

HAS BUTTERFINGERS DROPPED A BABY ON ITS HEAD? OR A HAMMER ON SOMEONE'S TOES?

NO! IT'S WORSE! A GIRL IS JOINING OUR CLASS!

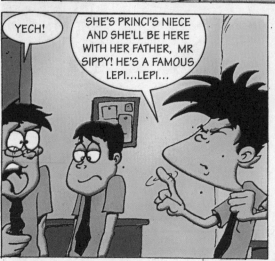

YECH!

SHE'S PRINCI'S NIECE AND SHE'LL BE HERE WITH HER FATHER, MR SIPPY! HE'S A FAMOUS LEPI...LEPI...

...LEPIDOPTERIST! A MAN WHO STUDIES BUTTERFLIES AND MOTHS!

HE'S ALSO A NATURE PHOTOGRAPHER. HE'S COMING HERE TO STUDY AND TAKE PHOTOGRAPHS OF THE RARE BUTTERFLIES ON TITLI HILL!

BUT WHY INFLICT HIS DAUGHTER ON US? WITH OUR LUCK, SHE'LL BE A BORING GOODY TWO SHOES...

...WITH NO INTERESTS EXCEPT FOR STUDIES AND HOMEWORK!

THE VERY NEXT WEEK, MINU, MR SIPPY'S DAUGHTER, ARRIVED.

HI GUYS! SORRY TO PILE ON TO YOU FOR A MONTH!

SHE LOOKS NICE!

HUMPH!

HEY, DID YOU GUYS SEE THE GERMANY-FRANCE MATCH ON TV LAST WEEK. IT WAS EXCITING, HUH?

Y...YOU LIKE FOOTBALL?!

SHE CAN'T BE SO BAD THEN!

I HEARD ABOUT THE FOOTBALL MATCH THAT YOU WON, THANKS TO BUTTERFINGERS'... ER... AMAR'S CLUMSINESS. I WISH I HAD SEEN IT!

OH, THAT'S NOT THE ONLY TIME HE'S BEEN CLUMSY!

SHUT UP, KIRAN!

DO YOU KNOW HE ONCE BROKE A VASE ON PRINCI'S...ER... YOUR UNCLE'S TABLE...

...AND THERE WAS THE TIME HE DROPPED A FAKE CENTIPEDE ON THE FLOOR....

THE BOYS REGALED MINU WITH BUTTERFINGERS' EXPLOITS...

...AND SOON, SHE WAS FIRM FRIENDS WITH ALL OF THEM. ONE DAY –

BUTTERFINGERS! HURRY UP! MY DAD'S GIVING A TALK ON BUTTERFLIES TODAY!

ER...COMING, MINU!

THE GOLDEN BIRDWING IS A RARE BREED, SPOTTED ONLY IN THIS DISTRICT. BUT THE MORE COMMON SWALLOW-TAIL AND BRUSH-FOOTED BUTTERFLIES ARE FOUND IN OTHER PARTS OF INDIA TOO....

I DIDN'T KNOW THERE WERE SO MANY BUTTERFLIES HERE! WE SHOULD START A BUTTERFLY CLUB!

GOOD IDEA!

15

WE'LL ASK SIVARAM THE GARDENER THE BEST PLACES TO SPOT BUTTERFLIES. HE'S A GREAT NATURE LOVER.

AND WE'LL TAKE DAD WITH US. HE CAN TELL US ALL ABOUT THE ONES WE SEE!

THE NEXT DAY—

I HOPE WE SPOT SOME UNUSUAL BUTTERFLIES! REMEMBER, IF YOU DO CATCH ONE, BRING IT TO ME. I'LL IDENTIFY IT AND THEN WE'LL RELEASE THE BUTTERFLY.

WE'LL KEEP OUR EYES PEELED, MR SIPPY!

AHA... BLUE SWALLOWTAIL! WHAT A BEAUTY!

I'VE GOT ONE! I'VE GOT ONE! LOOK, MR SIPPY!

THAT'S NOT A BUTTERFLY...IT'S A COMMON MOTH!

HA! HA! FOOLISH BOY!

TRUST YOU TO MAKE A MISTAKE LIKE THAT, BUTTER!

AFTER A WHILE—

I HAVEN'T SEEN ANY OF THE EXOTIC BUTTERFLIES I EXPECTED TO SPOT HERE...THE GOLDEN BIRDWING OR THE RED FRITILLARY...MAYBE I SHOULD TRY THAT HILL...

NO, NO! IT'S DANGEROUS! A...A LEOPARD HAS BEEN SEEN THERE!

16

REALLY? HOW STRANGE! BUT DON'T WORRY, I'LL BE CAREFUL!

WE'LL COME WITH YOU JUST IN CASE, DAD!

HMM...NO BUTTERFLIES HERE EITHER...THIS IS MOST UNUSUAL.

YES...YES... NOW LET'S GO BACK!

HEY, LOOK AT THAT LITTLE HUT! I WONDER WHO LIVES IN IT?

THERE ARE ALL SORTS OF BOXES HERE! AND BUTTERFLY NETS TOO!

WHAT DO YOU THINK THEY'RE STORING IN THIS BOX?

I DON'T CARE...LET'S GO! I DON'T WANT TO BE EATEN BY A LEOPARD!

LEOPARD?!!

LOOK AT ALL THE BUTTERFLIES!

Butterfingers' Masterpiece

Story: Khyrunnisa A.
Script: Gayathri Chandrasekaran
Illustrations: Abhijeet Kini

HEY GUYS, HAVE YOU HEARD THE LATEST? WE'RE GOING TO HAVE PAINTING IN SCHOOL.

OH, THAT SHOULD BE FUN... MY HOUSE WAS PAINTED JUST SOME WEEKS AGO. I'M QUITE GOOD AT IT!

REALLY, BUTTER! I THOUGHT YOUR DAD DIDN'T WANT YOU ANYWHERE CLOSE TO THE PAINT!

NOT THAT PAINTING, SILLY! I MEANT ART CLASSES.

ART CLASS?! WHO WANTS TO LEARN TO DRAW?! DRAWING IS FOR GIRLS AND SISSIES!

OH, SO ACCORDING TO YOU, PICASSO, MICHELANGELO, DA VINCI, DALI AND EVEN OUR OWN MR HUSAIN ARE ALL WOMEN!

I KNEW IT! YOU'RE AT THE BOTTOM OF THIS! YOU MUST'VE GIVEN PRINCI THIS GHASTLY IDEA!

WELL... HE DID ASK ME WHAT CLASSES I HAD IN MY SCHOOL IN FRANCE AND I MENTIONED ART AND MUSIC AND....

GROAN!!! THIS IS WHAT COMES OF HAVING GIRLS IN CLASS!

SSSHH! PEOPLE, PRINCI'S COMING!

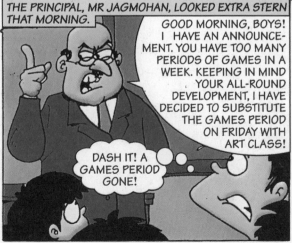

THE PRINCIPAL, MR JAGMOHAN, LOOKED EXTRA STERN THAT MORNING.

GOOD MORNING, BOYS! I HAVE AN ANNOUNCE-MENT. YOU HAVE TOO MANY PERIODS OF GAMES IN A WEEK. KEEPING IN MIND YOUR ALL-ROUND DEVELOPMENT, I HAVE DECIDED TO SUBSTITUTE THE GAMES PERIOD ON FRIDAY WITH ART CLASS!

DASH IT! A GAMES PERIOD GONE!

SIR, AS CAPTAIN OF THE CRICKET TEAM, I MUST PROTEST...

...AND I AM SURE EVERYBODY WILL COOPERATE WITH ME!

ULP!

THAT FRIDAY –

ART CLASS TODAY INSTEAD OF GAMES!

IT'S ONLY ONE GAMES PERIOD GONE. YOU NEVER KNOW, WE MAY ACTUALLY ENJOY IT!

TRAITORS!

THE ART PERIOD CAME SOON.

WOW! THE AUDITORIUM'S BEEN CONVERTED INTO OUR ART CLASS-ROOM.

THE EASELS ARE LINED UP SO BEAUTIFULLY.

HI BOYS! .... AND GIRL! MY NAME IS HIRAN KUMAR. I AM YOUR NEW ART TEACHER.

(GIGGLE!...)

NOW, I WANT YOU TO TAKE THESE CLASSES SERIOUSLY. YOU CAN DRAW, SKETCH AND DOODLE. BUT YOU MUST UNDERSTAND THAT PAINTING IS SERIOUS BUSINESS.

SERIOUS PAINTING REQUIRES PERSEVERANCE ALONG WITH TALENT. SO I WANT ALL OF YOU TO TRY HARD. BELIEVE IN YOURSELVES...

OOPS!

WATCH OUT!

CRASH

S..SORRY, SIR.

YOU'RE A DISASTER, BOY! NEVER MIND ... IT'S OKAY... WHAT'S YOUR NAME?

A... AMAR, SIR.

AMAR! THAT RINGS A BELL... ... OH YOU'RE THE ONE WHOM THE PRINCIPAL TOLD ME TO BEWARE OF! I CAN SEE WHY. AREN'T YOU THE ONE THE STUDENTS HAVE NICKNAMED...

... BUTTERFINGERS!

YES, BUTTERFINGERS! NOW WE MUSTN'T LET YOU SIT IN THE EPICENTRE OF A POSSIBLE EARTHQUAKE EVERY DAY. WE'LL MOVE YOU THERE BY THE WINDOW.

THANKS, SIR.

DECENT CHAP!

YEAH... RATHER FLAKY BUT FUN!

21

A MONTH DOWN THE LINE —

TODAY, WE'LL DO SOMETHING DIFFERENT. I WANT YOU TO DRAW A REALISTIC SCENE FROM LIFE. ANYTHING THAT YOU OBSERVE AROUND YOU. OKAY... LET'S GET ON....

BUT —

THE FIELDERS CAN STAND HERE. MAYBE BENJI AND KARAN SHOULD BE THE OPENERS. BUT IF THEY BOWL SPIN IN THE MIDDLE, I'LL NEED BENJI ... SO IT SHOULD BE KARAN AND RAGHAV MAYBE...

TIME'S UP, KIDS. LET ME SEE WHAT YOU'VE DRAWN.

(GASP!)...

CRICKET MATCH? WHERE ARE THE PLAYERS?

CRICKET MATCH

AND WHAT ARE ALL THESE DOWNWARD STROKES SUPPOSED TO MEAN?

CRICKET MATCH

THAT'S RAIN, SIR... THE MATCH HAS BEEN WASHED OUT BY RAIN.

ENOUGH!! THIS WON'T DO! HOW DARE YOU PULL A TEACHER'S LEG???

CRICKET MATCH

IT'S OKAY, MR JAGMOHAN. BOYS WILL BE BOYS....

HUSH! DON'T SUPPORT THEM. I'LL DEAL WITH THIS.

22

YOU WILL NOT GIVE SMART ANSWERS, AMAR! WHY HAVE YOU NOT DONE YOUR PAINTING?

I... I WAS THINKING OF THE CRICKET MATCH, SIR.

CRICKET! CRICKET! CRICKET! THAT'S ALL YOU CAN THINK ABOUT!

I'M TRYING HARD TO ENSURE THAT YOU KIDS GET AN ALL-ROUND EDUCATION HERE AND WHAT DO I GET IN RETURN? THIS! NO, AMAR... NEXT WEEK I WILL COME ROUND AND SEE WHAT YOU HAVE DRAWN. AND IF IT IS NOT UP TO THE MARK, NO MORE CRICKET FOR YOU!

TOUGH LUCK, KID! JUST PRACTISE HARD!

AMAR PRACTISED LIKE A MAN OBSESSED!

MMM... MUST IMPROVE THE COW'S FACE, ITS BODY AND THE TAIL. AND MAYBE THE LEGS TOO... THE REST IS FINE!

HEY! WHERE'S ALL THE BUTTER PAPER I HAD KEPT FOR STORING MY CAKES?!

ULP!

SHOVE

THE WEEK PASSED IN NO TIME AND SOON –

ARE YOU ALL SET?

Y..YES, I THINK!

ALL THE BEST, CHUM!

23

MR JAGMOHAN CAME WITH A VISITOR.

CHILDREN, THIS IS THE FAMOUS PAINTER, MR HABIB SHAH. HE WILL BE LOOKING AT YOUR WORK TODAY.

THE CLASS WORKED FURIOUSLY. AMAR PAINTED IN DEAD EARNEST.

TIME'S ALMOST UP... I AM GOING TO BOWL PRINCI OVER WITH MY PAINTING....

LET'S SEE....

OOPS!

OH, NO!!!!

TWO MINUTES MORE.

DRAT! WHAT DO I DO NOW?

THINK, THINK.... THINK AMAR!

OKAY, MR SHAH WILL LOOK AT YOUR WORK NOW.

SOON – HMMM....

INTERESTING....

MR JAGMOHAN AND MR HIRAN... I MUST CONGRATULATE YOU... YOU HAVE A GENIUS IN YOUR SCHOOL! THIS BOY'S BRILLIANT... LOOK AT THE BOLD USE OF COLOURS AND THE FLAMBOYANT BRUSH STROKES! HE IS A TRUE ARTIST! WONDERFUL!

???

ER... GENIUS.. YES....

WHAT'S YOUR NAME, BOY?

BUTTER... ER.. AMAR!

HE CAN'T REMEMBER HIS OWN NAME... ABSENT-MINDED, HUH?! SO HOW DID YOU THINK OF CREATING THIS TODAY?

ER... I... ER... WAS INSPIRED BY MR HIRAN'S T-SHIRT.

BRILLIANT! GREAT JOB, AMAR! I HAD TOLD MR JAGMOHAN THAT I WOULD GIVE A SMALL PRIZE TO THE STUDENT WHOSE WORK I REALLY LIKE... AND IT GOES TO YOU!

T... THANKS, SIR.

SO MR ARTIST, WHAT'S THE BIG, EXCITING THING THAT YOU ARE GOING TO DO NEXT?

PLAY A CRICKET MATCH, SIR!

HE'S AN ALL-ROUNDER!

THAT HE IS...HA HA HA!

Butterfingers Gets A Haircut

Story: Khyrunnisa A.
Script: Anomita Guha
Illustrations: Abhijeet Kini
Colourist: Rajesh Phatak

AMAR (aka BUTTERFINGERS) AND HIS FRIENDS HAVE JUST FINISHED THEIR EXAMS –

HEY, GUYS! THAT WAS A PRETTY TOUGH PAPER, WASN'T IT?

THAT LAST QUESTION WAS GREEK TO ME! I'M SURE I MESSED IT UP!

WHAT DOES IT MATTER? THE EXAMS ARE O-V-E-R....

OOPS!

BUTTERFINGERS! YOU NEARLY TOOK MY HEAD OFF!

WELL, YOU SHOULDN'T HAVE BEEN STANDING THERE! I DIDN'T SEE YOU!

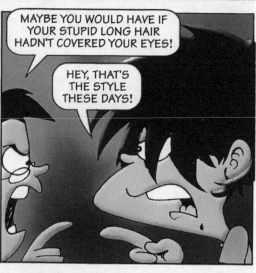

MAYBE YOU WOULD HAVE IF YOUR STUPID LONG HAIR HADN'T COVERED YOUR EYES!

HEY, THAT'S THE STYLE THESE DAYS!

STOP FIGHTING, GUYS! WE'VE GOT MORE IMPORTANT THINGS TO DISCUSS...LIKE THE END-OF-TERM ROCK CONCERT!

YES, I CAN'T BELIEVE PRINCI AGREED TO IT!

THE COOLEST ROCK BAND IN TOWN, THE HEEBEE JEEBEES, WILL ACTUALLY BE PERFORMING AT OUR VERY OWN SCHOOL!

I'VE NEVER HEARD THEIR SONGS BEFORE! ARE THEY REALLY THAT GOOD?

HeeBee JeeBees LIVE!! BE THERE !!!

THEY'RE AMAZING! AND EVERY TIME THEY PERFORM, THEY PICK OUT ONE LUCKY PERSON IN THE AUDIENCE, WHO WINS AUTOGRAPHED CDs AND POSTERS!

IT'S OUR MISSION TO MAKE SURE IT'S ONE OF US THIS TIME!

AT THE HEEBEE JEEBEES' LAST CONCERT, THE GUY WEARING THE MOST COLOURFUL SHIRT GOT SELECTED!

AND THE YEAR BEFORE THAT, THEY CHOSE A GIRL WITH THE LONGEST NOSE!

HMM...IT'S CLEAR THAT WE'LL HAVE TO DO SOMETHING TO STAND OUT IN THE CROWD!

(GIGGLE!)... MAYBE BUTTERFINGERS WILL WIN FOR BEING THE MOST ACCIDENT-PRONE PERSON THERE!

VERY FUNNY!

LET'S JUST DRESS UP IN THE BRIGHTEST AND WEIRDEST CLOTHES WE CAN FIND AND HOPE FOR THE BEST!

SOUNDS LIKE A GOOD PLAN TO ME!

ME TOO!

HUMPH! WITH OUR LUCK, THE BAND WILL PROBABLY PICK OUT SOME NERD IN A SCHOOL UNIFORM THIS YEAR!

HJ

LATER AT HOME –

SO, AMAR, HOW WAS YOUR EXAM TODAY?

ULP...NOT BAD, DAD!

NOT BAD?! OR NOT GQOD? HOW COULD YOU EVEN READ YOUR QUESTION PAPER WITH YOUR HAIR FALLING ALL OVER YOUR EYES LIKE THAT?!

BUT DAD...IT MAKES ME LOOK COOL!

IT MAKES YOU LOOK LIKE A FOOL! WE'LL GO TOMORROW MORNING TO THE BARBER.

B...BUT THE CONCERT IS TOMORROW MORNING! I CAN'T MISS THAT!

HAIRCUT FIRST, AND THEN THE CONCERT! I WANT A HUMAN FOR A SON, NOT A SHAGGY POODLE!

(GROAN!)... WHY DO THESE THINGS HAPPEN ONLY TO ME?!

I'LL HAVE TO MAKE DAD HURRY UP TOMORROW SO I DON'T MISS THE CONCERT!

THE NEXT MORNING –

GRMPH... WHO IS IT?

KNOCK! KNOCK!

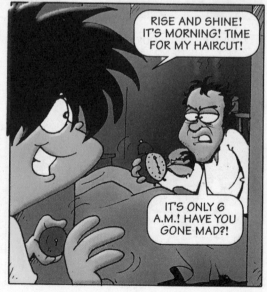

RISE AND SHINE! IT'S MORNING! TIME FOR MY HAIRCUT!

IT'S ONLY 6 A.M.! HAVE YOU GONE MAD?!

28

BUT YOU ALWAYS SAID EARLY TO RISE MAKES A MAN HEALTHY, WEALTHY AND WISE!

NEVER MIND WHAT I SAID! GO BACK TO SLEEP AND STOP BOTHERING ME!

AT BREAKFAST –

DAD, DO YOU WANT SOME TOAST? SOME JAM? WHY DON'T YOU GET DRESSED WHILE I BUTTER YOUR TOAST FOR YOU?

!!!

AMAR, STOP HARASSING YOUR FATHER! LET HIM HAVE HIS BREAKFAST IN PEACE.

FINE, MA ...BUT TIME'S TICKING AWAY! THE CONCERT STARTS AT TEN AND IT'S ALREADY NINE!

HALF AN HOUR LATER –

WELL, AMAR, YOU'VE MANAGED TO DRAG ME TO THE BARBERSHOP WITHOUT ALLOWING ME TO FINISH MY COFFEE!

SORRY, DAD! BUT IT'S URGENT!

WHAT KIND OF STYLE WOULD YOU LIKE? CREWCUT, BUZZ, SPIKY....

ANY! JUST CUT MY HAIR!

HMM....

CUT IT QUICKLY!

SNIP!

29

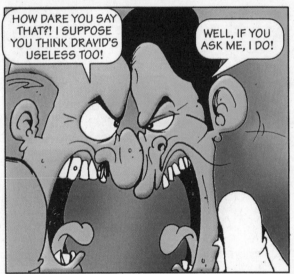

OW! MY FOOT!

MY HAIR!

GASP! IT'S 10 O'CLOCK!

I HAVE TO GO! BYE, DAD!

!!!

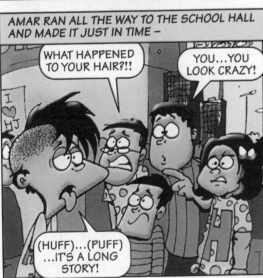

AMAR RAN ALL THE WAY TO THE SCHOOL HALL AND MADE IT JUST IN TIME –

WHAT HAPPENED TO YOUR HAIR?!!

YOU...YOU LOOK CRAZY!

(HUFF)...(PUFF) ...IT'S A LONG STORY!

HEY, HEY! THE SUN'S OUT TODAY! SO LET'S GO OUT AND PLAYEEE....

I'LL TELL YOU LATER! LET'S WATCH THE CONCERT!

THE HEEBEE JEEBEES PERFORMED ALL OF THEIR GREATEST HITS TO LOUD APPLAUSE AND AT THE END –

OUR WINNER TODAY IS SPECIAL! THIS GUY HAS THE GUTS TO CARRY OFF A HAIRCUT THAT NO ONE ELSE COULD! YOU, COME UP HERE!

CONGRATS! YOU WIN THESE AUTO-GRAPHED CDs! AND WE'RE GOING TO GET HAIRSTYLES JUST LIKE YOURS FOR OUR NEXT CONCERT!

HURRAH FOR BUTTERFINGERS!

AND HIS HAIR!

CLAP! CLAP!

31

BUTTERFINGERS and the CACTUS

Story: Khyrunnisa A
Script: Anomita Guha
Illustrations & Colouring: Abhijeet Kini

2X + 3Y (A-B) IS EQUAL TO…

…ONE BIG HEADACHE!

MR SAHA, CAN I SPEAK TO YOU FOR A MOMENT?

OF COURSE, MR JAGMOHAN.

CLASS, CONTINUE WITH YOUR SUMS AND NO TALKING!

UH-OH, BUTTERFINGERS, PRINCI'S GOT THAT LOOK ON HIS FACE!

WHAT LOOK?

THE LOOK THAT MEANS HE HAS SOME AWFUL SCHEME UP HIS SLEEVE!

YOU MEAN, LIKE WHEN HE REPLACED OUR GAMES PERIOD WITH ART CLASS?

ART CLASS WASN'T SO BAD! IT COULD BE WORSE THIS TIME…MAYBE HE'S ASKING MR SAHA TO GIVE US A SURPRISE MATHS TEST!

HORRORS! DON'T SAY SUCH SCARY THINGS, MINU! I'LL GET NIGHTMARES ABOUT IT!

CLASS, PAY ATTENTION! I'VE BEEN TALKING TO MR SAHA ABOUT ARRANGING A SPECIAL PROJECT FOR YOU.

SPECIAL PROJECT?!

I HOPE IT'S NOT ANOTHER WAY OF SAYING WE HAVE MORE HOMEWORK!

RECENTLY, I ATTENDED A SEMINAR ON 'EARTH, THE GREEN PLANET'...

BUT, SIR, EARTH'S KNOWN AS THE BLUE PLANET!

CRASH!

AMAR, MUST YOU ALWAYS BE SO CLUMSY?! BESIDES, I WAS TALKING ABOUT EARTH FROM AN ENVIRONMENTAL POINT OF VIEW!

OH! SORRY, SIR!

I THINK ALL OF YOU CAN CONTRIBUTE TO MAKING OUR SCHOOL GREENER, BY GROWING MORE PLANTS AND FLOWERS...BOTH OUTDOORS AND INDOORS!

OUTDOORS?!

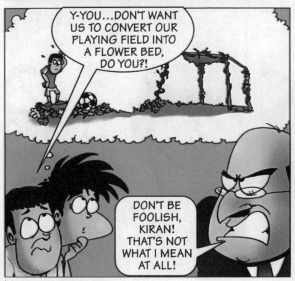

Y-YOU...DON'T WANT US TO CONVERT OUR PLAYING FIELD INTO A FLOWER BED, DO YOU?!

DON'T BE FOOLISH, KIRAN! THAT'S NOT WHAT I MEAN AT ALL!

NOW, YOU CAN EITHER HELP THE GARDENER MAINTAIN THE LAWNS AND FLOWER BEDS OR YOU CAN TAKE CARE OF HOUSE PLANTS INSIDE THE SCHOOL.

IT'S ENTIRELY UP TO YOU BUT WHATEVER YOU CHOOSE, YOU MUST DO IT WELL!

AFTER CLASS –

HELPING THE GARDENER IS OUT OF THE QUESTION! HE STILL HATES ME AFTER WHAT HAPPENED LAST YEAR!

YEAH... BUTTERFINGERS DECIDED TO HELP HIM WATER THE ROSES...

...HE DROPPED THE HOSE... AND THE REST IS HISTORY!

AAARGH!

BUTTER, YOU'D BETTER BE MORE CAREFUL THIS TIME! LET'S CHOOSE THE INDOOR OPTION AND KEEP A POTTED PLANT...

WHERE? ON YOUR HEAD?!

VERY FUNNY, KIRAN!

WHAT SORT OF PLANT SHOULD WE HAVE? MAYBE A TULSI PLANT OR SOME KIND OF FERN...

NO! GUYS, I KNOW EXACTLY WHAT WE SHOULD GET...A CACTUS!

BUT WHY? CACTUS...ER... CACTUSES... ..ER..ER..CACTI ...ARE UGLY! THEY'RE PRICKLY AND KNOBBLY AND HAVE TERRIBLY SHARP SPINES...

YOU HAVEN'T LISTED THEIR BEST QUALITY... THEY NEED VERY LITTLE CARE!

ALL WE NEED TO DO IS PLACE THE CACTUS IN SUNLIGHT AND WATER IT ONCE IN A WHILE AND IT WILL FLOURISH!

GREAT IDEA, BUTTER!

MY MOTHER'S GOT A CACTUS COLLECTION AT HOME. I'M SURE SHE WON'T MIND LENDING US ONE TO KEEP AT SCHOOL

THEN IT'S DECIDED! A CACTUS IT IS!

THE NEXT DAY –

CAREFUL, BUTTER! DON'T YOU DARE DROP THE CACTUS ON MY FOOT!

WHY DON'T YOU WATCH WHERE YOU'RE GOING INSTEAD OF NAGGING ME ALL THE TIME...

WILL YOU BOYS BE CAREFUL?! YOU COULD TAKE OUT SOMEONE'S EYE WITH THAT CACTUS!

GULP! YES, SIR!

PRINCI'S AS PRICKLY AS OUR CACTUS! WHAT'S THE MATTER WITH HIM ANYWAY? WHY IS HE SO GRUMPY TODAY?

HAVEN'T YOU TWO HEARD?

PRINCI WAS IN A VERY GOOD MOOD A FEW DAYS AGO...

SORRY, I'M LATE, SIR...

OH, NO PROBLEM, ERIC! NOW RUN ALONG BEFORE YOU'RE EVEN LATER!

WAIT A MINUTE...HE MADE ME COPY OUT 200 LINES AS PUNISHMENT THE OTHER DAY!

WELL, HE USUALLY GIVES YOU 500 LINES SO HE MUST HAVE BEEN FEELING HAPPY! GO ON, ERIC...

PRINCI WAS IN SUCH A GOOD MOOD BECAUSE HE HAD RECEIVED A LETTER FROM AN OLD SCHOOL FRIEND –

TUBBY'S WRITTEN TO ME! OH, IT'S BEEN YEARS SINCE I SAW HIM!

I WONDER HOW HE TRACED ME. HE SAYS HE'LL BE IN TOWN FOR A FEW DAYS AND WANTS TO MEET UP. I CAN CALL HIM AT THE NUMBER GIVEN HERE...

UNFORTUNATELY, PRINCI LOST THE LETTER! HE HAD KEPT IT ON HIS DESK BUT IT FELL ACCIDENTALLY INTO THE DUSTBIN...

...THE SWEEPER SWEPT IT AWAY AND THE GARDENER BURNT IT WITH THE OTHER RUBBISH!

POOR PRINCI! NO WONDER HE SNAPPED AT US!

LET'S HIDE THIS CACTUS IN A CORNER SOMEWHERE FOR THE TIME BEING... IT SEEMS TO IRRITATE HIM!

THIS IS A GOOD SPOT. PRINCI WON'T EVEN NOTICE IT HERE!

NOW LET'S GO BACK TO CLASS BEFORE WE RUN INTO PRINCI AGAIN...

W...WATCH OUT!

37

LATER, AT THE HOSPITAL –

PRINCI'S GOING TO EXPEL ME FOR SURE THIS TIME... I'M THE ONLY STUDENT WHO'S MANAGED TO LAND HIM IN HOSPITAL!

DON'T WORRY, BUTTER! YOU CAN ER.. BUTTER HIM UP WITH THOSE FLOWERS!

AMAR, MY DEAR BOY, COME IN! I'M SO GLAD TO SEE YOU!

HUH?!

DID PRINCI HURT HIS HEAD?!

TUBBY, THIS IS THE BOY I WAS TELLING YOU ABOUT. I FELL DOWN THE STAIRS BECAUSE OF HIS CLUMSINESS! AND WHAT A FALL IT WAS...IT REUNITED ME WITH YOU!

IT...IT DID?

THIS IS TUBBY...ER... MAHINDER, AN OLD FRIEND OF MINE. I HAD NO WAY OF CONTACTING HIM AFTER I LOST HIS LETTER. BUT WHEN I ENTERED THE HOSPITAL, GUESS WHO I FOUND IN THE NEXT BED!

ME! YOU CAN IMAGINE HOW THRILLED I WAS TO SEE CACTUS!

CACTUS?!

YES, THAT WAS YOUR PRINCIPAL'S NICKNAME IN SCHOOL. HE USED TO BE QUITE TOUCHY, YOU KNOW!

AHEM!

WHAT A COINCIDENCE THAT A CACTUS BROUGHT MAHINDER AND CACTUS...ER... PRINCIPAL JAGMOHAN TOGETHER AGAIN!

A CACTUS....AND BUTTERFINGERS!

New Shoes for Butterfingers

Story: Khyrunnisa A
Script: Anomita Guha
Illustrations and Colouring: Abhijeet Kini

AMAR (ALSO KNOWN AS BUTTERFINGERS) WAS RUSHING TO SCHOOL ONE DAY –

HI MA! BYE, MA!

WAIT A SECOND!

YOU'RE NOT GOING ANYWHERE WITH THOSE SHOES!

WHY NOT? THEY'RE JUST A BIT WORN OUT...AND MUDDY ... BUT THAT'S ALL!

THEY'RE FALLING APART IN FRONT OF MY EYES!

SHE'S RIGHT, SON. I'VE SEEN TRAMPS WITH BETTER FOOTWEAR!

AMAR, I'VE TOLD YOU TIME AND AGAIN TO BUY NEW SHOES...I'VE EVEN GIVEN YOU THE MONEY FOR THEM!

I'LL PICK UP A NEW PAIR AFTER SCHOOL, I PROMISE! BYE!

AT SCHOOL –

WHAT'S PRINCI DOING IN CLASS? WE HAVEN'T DONE ANYTHING TO GET IN TROUBLE THIS WEEK, HAVE WE?!

NO, HE'S JUST COME TO ANNOUNCE SOMETHING!

STUDENTS, I'M PLEASED TO TELL YOU THAT OUR NEW SPORTS CENTRE HAS BEEN COMPLETED.

THAT MEANS BUTTER WILL BE DROPPING TENNIS RACKETS INSTEAD OF BOOKS AND PAINTBRUSHES!

I'VE ASKED A SPECIAL GUEST TO INAUGURATE IT TODAY AT FOUR... A FAMOUS SPORTSMAN...

WHO? SACHIN? BAICHUNG? RONALDO?!!

MR ASHWIN KUMAR!!

WOW! HE'S THE BEST TENNIS PLAYER IN THE COUNTRY! HE WON THE GOLD MEDAL AT THE OLYMPICS...THE DAVIS CUP...

...AND BEST OF ALL, HE WON THE FRENCH OPEN THIS YEAR!

YES...YES...YOU ALL SEEM WELL VERSED WITH HIS ACHIEVEMENTS!

NOW, ONE OF YOU MUST FORMALLY INTRODUCE HIM ... AMAR, WILL YOU DO IT?

GASP! ME? SHARE THE STAGE WITH ASHWIN KUMAR! I CAN'T BELIEVE IT! HE'LL BE STANDING RIGHT BESIDE ME!

OW!

CRASH!

DO TRY TO CONTAIN YOUR EXCITEMENT, BOY!

ER... YES, SIR! DON'T WORRY, I'LL BE ON MY BEST BEHAVIOUR FROM NOW ON!

GOOD...AND AMAR, YOU MUST BE WELL TURNED OUT FOR THE EVENT. YOUR HAIR MUST BE TIDY, YOUR SHOES WELL POLISHED...

ER...YES, SIR...

(GASP!) YOUR SHOES ARE DISGUSTING! YOU CAN'T WELCOME ASHWIN KUMAR IN THEM! HE'LL THINK OUR STUDENTS ARE SLOBS!

I...I WAS GOING TO BUY NEW ONES...

YOU MUST RUSH TO THE SHOE STORE AFTER SCHOOL AND PICK UP A NEW PAIR....BUT BE SURE YOU RETURN BY FIVE!

Y...YES...SIR!

IN THE AFTERNOON –

I'VE WASHED MY FACE AND TUCKED IN MY SHIRT...

...AND WE'VE COMBED YOUR HAIR AS NEATLY AS WE COULD!

YOU LOOK ALMOST PRESENTABLE ...EXCEPT FOR YOUR ICKY SHOES!

RELAX, I'LL BE BACK WEARING A SHINY NEW PAIR IN HALF AN HOUR!·

BUT WHEN AMAR REACHED THE SHOE STORE –

BOXES EVERYWHERE! WHAT'S GOING ON HERE?!

WE'RE IN THE MIDDLE OF RENOVATING THE SHOP...BUT DON'T WORRY, I'LL HELP YOU FIND WHAT YOU'RE LOOKING FOR.

41

JAI, COME HERE! THIS LADY WANTS TO SEE THE BLUE-GREEN KOLHAPURI CHAPPALS IN SIZE SEVEN!

ER:... EXCUSE ME...

HOPE HE DOESN'T TAKE TOO LONG TO GET BACK...

UNACCEPTABLE! THIS IS TOTALLY UNACCEPTABLE!

I SEND MY MOST PRECIOUS PAIR OF SHOES...MY LUCKY PAIR... TO YOU FOR MINOR REPAIRS AND WHAT DO YOU DO?! YOU LOSE THEM!

SIR, PLEASE CALM DOWN! THEY'RE NOT LOST EXACTLY ...THEY'VE JUST BEEN MISPLACED!

ACCEPT A REPLACEMENT FROM ANY BRAND YOU LIKE!

I WILL NOT! I NEED MY LUCKY SHOES FOR A MATCH ON TUESDAY AND NO OTHER PAIR WILL DO!

JAI, DINESH ...STOP WHATEVER YOU'RE DOING AT ONCE AND LOOK FOR THOSE SHOES!

YES, SIR!

LOOKS LIKE THE SALESMEN ARE GOING TO BE BUSY FOR A WHILE...I'LL HAVE TO HELP MYSELF!

OUCH... THESE ARE TOO SMALL!

...AND THESE ARE TOO BIG!

I'M BEGINNING TO FEEL LIKE GOLDILOCKS! HOW WILL I FIND A PAIR THAT'S JUST RIGHT?!

THERE ARE MORE SHOES UP HERE...

WHAT'S THAT BOY DOING?!

I...OOOPS!

YIKES!

WHAT HAVE YOU DONE, YOU CLUMSY BOY!

I...I...I...

43

MY SHOES! MY LUCKY SHOES! YOU'VE FOUND THEM!

A...ASHWIN K...KUMAR?!

I'VE WORN THESE DURING EVERY MAJOR TITLE AND I'VE NEVER LOST SO FAR! OH, I'M SO HAPPY I'VE GOT THEM BACK!

YES..ER... GOOD JOB, BOY!

IS THERE ANYTHING I CAN DO FOR YOU IN RETURN?

OH NO, SIR! ALL I WANTED IS TO BUY A NEW PAIR OF SHOES SO I COULD WEAR THEM WHEN I INTRODUCED YOU AT OUR SCHOOL'S NEW SPORTS CENTRE!

(GASP!)... WITH ALL MY WORRY ABOUT MY SHOES, I'D ALMOST FORGOTTEN ABOUT THE INAUGURATION. WE MUST HURRY!

GET HIM SOME SHOES AT ONCE, THE BEST YOU HAVE! I'LL PAY FOR THEM!

YES, SIR!

AT THE INAUGURATION –

PLEASE WELCOME WORLD-FAMOUS TENNIS PLAYER – ASHWIN KUMAR!

THANK YOU, AMAR!

CLAP! CLAP! CLAP! CLAP! CLAP!

SMART BOY, THAT! WITH STUDENTS LIKE HIM, THIS SCHOOL WILL GO A LONG WAY!

!!!

BUTTERFINGERS AT SCHOOL

Story: Khyrunnisa A.
Script: Anomita Guha
Illustrations: Abhijeet Kini
Colouring: Umesh Sarode

AMAR'S MOTHER HAD JUST RETURNED HOME FROM VISITING HER FRIEND DEEPA –

THAT MRS SINGH REALLY GETS MY GOAT! BOASTING FOR HOURS ABOUT HER BRILLIANT SON, MUNNA! SHE DIDN'T LET ME OR DEEPA GET A WORD IN EDGEWISE!

WHO'S THIS WOMAN?

SHE'S DEEPA'S NEW NEIGHBOUR. MUNNA, HER SON, HAS RECENTLY JOINED AMAR'S SCHOOL.

HMM…AMAR HASN'T MENTIONED ANY MUNNA AT SCHOOL. I SUPPOSE HE HASN'T MET HIM YET.

FIRST IN CLASS AND QUIZZES, ELOCUTION AND DEBATE CHAMP, WINNER OF THE GOOD CONDUCT MEDAL – YOU NAME IT, HER MUNNA DARLING'S WON IT!

WHEW! WHO'S THIS PARAGON OF VIRTUE, MA?

SOME CHILD CALLED MUNNA! UFF! I CAN'T BELIEVE THAT WOMAN TALKED OUR EARS OFF FOR SO LONG!

YOU SHOULD'VE BRAGGED TO HER ABOUT OUR BUTTERFINGERS! ALWAYS GOOD AT BEING CLUMSY AND GETTING INTO TROUBLE!

VERY FUNNY, DAD! YOU KNOW I HAVEN'T HAD AN ACCIDENT IN AGES….

YIKES!

CRASH!

OH, AMAR! NOT AGAIN!

SORRY!

THE NEXT DAY –

MA! THERE'S A PARENT-TEACHER MEETING THIS AFTERNOON AT SCHOOL! THE TEACHERS WANT TO DISCUSS OUR MONTHLY REPORTS!

WHAT TIME DOES THE MEETING START?

AT THREE, BUT YOU SHOULD GO EARLY. I...I'M SURE MY TEACHERS WILL HAVE A LOT TO SAY TO YOU!

OH, DEAR! I HOPE YOU HAVEN'T MASTERMINDED ANY MAJOR DISASTERS RECENTLY!

NOT ANY MORE THAN USUAL! CAN I PICK SOME APPLES FROM THE GARDEN, MA?

ALL RIGHT, BUT BE CAREFUL!

MA'LL GET A BIG SURPRISE TODAY! SHE WON'T EXPECT....

YIKES!

AMAR, I'M JUST LEAVING... WHICH DIVISION ARE YOU IN?

BEEEEEEEEE!

DIVISION B, I MUST REMEMBER THAT!

SPLASH!

AT AMAR'S SCHOOL, IN CLASS IX B –

KARAN'S IMPROVED A LOT...HASN'T DROPPED A TEST TUBE IN WEEKS!

THIS FELLOW MUST BE THE CHEMISTRY TEACHER! AMAR'S GOOD AT SCIENCE SO I'LL START WITH HIM!

ER...MR SUBRAMANIAM, I'M AMAR'S MOTHER. HE'S IN DIVISION B...

AMAR?! THE BOY WHO SET MY LAB ON FIRE?!

FOOLING AROUND WITH FORMULAS HE KNOWS NOTHING ABOUT! HE'S A MORTAL DANGER TO US ALL!

GULP! I KNEW HE WAS CLUMSY BUT...

NO BUTS! AMAR KNOWS LESS SCIENCE THAN AN ANT! AND DOESN'T SEEM TO CARE ABOUT IT EITHER!

TRYING TO HIDE HER SHOCK, BUTTERFINGERS' MOTHER MOVED TO THE NEXT TEACHER –

ER...MY SON'S NAME IS AMAR...HE'S IN DIVISION B...

AMAR?! THAT BOY MAKES NO EFFORT AT ALL. HIS HOMEWORK'S A DISGRACE!

B...BUT AT LEAST HE TRIES HIS BEST, DOESN'T HE?

HUMPH! IF THIS IS HIS BEST, I'D BE SCARED TO SEE HIS WORST!

DUST BIN

AS AMAR'S MOTHER WENT FROM TEACHER TO TEACHER, THE REPORTS ONLY GOT WORSE!

...AND THE ONLY NUMBER HE SEEMS TO RECOGNIZE IS ZERO!

GASP!

HIS HANDWRITING LOOKS LIKE SPIDERS CRAWLING ACROSS THE PAGE...

OH NO!

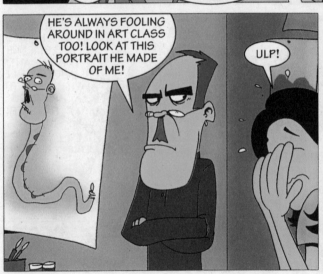

HE'S ALWAYS FOOLING AROUND IN ART CLASS TOO! LOOK AT THIS PORTRAIT HE MADE OF ME!

ULP!

AMAR'S MOTHER RETURNED HOME IN A FURIOUS MOOD –

AMAR, WHERE ARE YOU?!

WAIT TILL I GET MY HANDS ON HIM!

HI, MA! DID YOU HAVE A NICE TIME AT SCHOOL?

NICE TIME?! IT WAS A DISASTER! THE IX B TEACHERS HAD THE MOST UNPLEASANT THINGS TO SAY ABOUT YOUR WORK!

HUH?! BUT I...WAIT, MA! DID YOU SAY YOU WENT TO THE IX B CLASSROOM? I'M IN IX A!

Y...YOU DON'T MEAN...

YOU WENT TO THE WRONG CLASSROOM! THERE'S AN AMAR IN DIVISION B. THE TEACHERS MUST HAVE THOUGHT YOU WERE HIS MOTHER!

B...BUT YOU SAID YOU WERE IN DIVISION B! I ASKED YOU WHEN I WAS LEAVING!

OH! YOU MUST HAVE ASKED ME WHEN THOSE BEES WERE CHASING ME! I WAS LUCKY THEY DIDN'T STING ME!

WAIT...SO THE TEACHERS WEREN'T TALKING ABOUT YOU?

OF COURSE NOT! I SLOGGED THIS TERM TO SURPRISE YOU, MA...AND I GOT THE HIGHEST MARKS IN ALL SUBJECTS BUT HINDI!

BUT THEN WHO'S THIS OTHER AMAR? A NEW STUDENT?

YES...HE'S A NICE, BRIGHT KID, MA. BUT HIS MOTHER PUSHES HIM SO HARD, HE'S TURNED TOTALLY REBELLIOUS!

POOR CHILD. EVEN SO, I'D BETTER CALL HIS MOTHER TO WARN HER ABOUT HIS HORRIBLE PERFORMANCE!

YOU CAN ASK DEEPA AUNTY, SHE'LL HAVE THE NUMBER...

AMAR'S THE SON OF HER NEIGHBOUR, MRS. SINGH...

MUNNA DARLING!!

THE END

49

BUTTERFINGERS AND THE SWIMMING POOL INCIDENT

Story: Khyrunnisa A.
Script: Anomita Guha
Illustrations and Colouring: Abhijeet Kini

BUTTERFINGERS! DO YOU KNOW WHY PRINCI'S CALLED A SPECIAL ASSEMBLY TODAY?

WE THOUGHT IT MIGHT BE BECAUSE YOU'VE GOT INTO TROUBLE AGAIN!

DON'T BE SILLY! YOU TWO MAKE IT SOUND AS IF I'M ALWAYS IN TROUBLE WHEN I NEVER...

CAREFUL!

CAUTION SLIPPERY WHEN WET

YIKES!

AMAR!

WHAT DO YOU THINK YOU'RE DOING?! YOU KNOW VERY WELL THAT SKATING IN THE HALLS IS FORBIDDEN!

B...BUT I WASN'T SKATING!

IF YOU WANT TO TAKE UP A SPORT, I SUGGEST YOU TRY SWIMMING! THAT'S WHAT OUR NEW POOL IS FOR!

(GULP!) YES, SIR! I'LL PRACTISE EVERY DAY!

AT THE ASSEMBLY –

WHAT DOES PRINCI CARE IF YOU CAN SWIM OR NOT?

HYUK! MAYBE HE WANTS TO TRAIN BUTTERFINGERS FOR THE OLYMPICS!

GOOD AFTERNOON EVERYBODY!

(AHEM!)... AS YOU ALL KNOW, WE HAVE A LARGE NEW SWIMMING POOL. I'M HAPPY TO SAY, OUR SCHOOL HAS BEEN SELECTED FOR THE HONOUR OF HOSTING THE INTER-DISTRICT SWIMMING CHAMPIONSHIPS!

SINCE OUR SCHOOL WILL BE TAKING PART IN THE SWIMMING COMPETITIONS, I WANT ALL OF YOU TO REDOUBLE YOUR EFFORTS AT PRACTICE TIME!

ULP!

PRINCI'S GONE MAD, ENTERING US INTO A SWIMMING COMPETITION LIKE THAT! HE KNOWS THAT NONE OF US CAN SWIM WELL!

YES...AND SOME OF US ARE STILL LEARNING HOW TO SWIM WITH FLOATS!

WE WON'T WIN A SINGLE EVENT AND WE'LL BECOME THE LAUGHING STOCK OF THE ENTIRE DISTRICT!

WE'VE GOT TO DO SOMETHING ABOUT THIS!

I'VE GOT AN IDEA! TWO NEW STUDENTS HAVE JOINED THIS TERM. MAYBE, JUST MAYBE, THEY CAN SWIM WELL!

LET'S FIND OUT RIGHT NOW!

AND SO –

MY DAD TAUGHT ME THE BUTTERFLY STROKE, THE BACK STROKE AND THE BREAST STROKE...

REALLY?!

SPLUTTER! SPLUTTER!

!!!!

I DON'T THINK WE CAN EXPECT THE WINNING STROKE FROM HIM!

ACHOO!

HOW ABOUT YOU, SALMAN? CAN YOU SWIM?

N...NO... NO! I...I HATE THE WATER!

NO NEED TO GET SO SCARED...IT'S NOT LIKE WE'RE GOING TO TOSS YOU INTO THE DEEP END OF THE POOL!

D...DON'T SAY THAT! PL...PLEASE DON'T!

YOU'RE SHAKING! WHAT'S THE MATTER?

I...I USED TO LOVE SWIMMING! I USED TO SPEND MORE TIME IN THE WATER THAN ON LAND!

THEN ONE DAY, SOMEONE ACCIDENTALLY PUSHED ME INTO THE POOL. I HURT MY HEAD BADLY AND...AND ALMOST DROWNED!

GASP!

I'VE NEVER STEPPED INTO WATER SINCE THEN!

DON'T WORRY, SALMAN. WE'LL FIND SOMEONE ELSE TO REPRESENT OUR SCHOOL.

BUT AFTER A WEEK OF LOOKING FOR CHAMPION SWIMMERS, THE GANG HAD TO ADMIT DEFEAT –

NO MEDALS FOR US TOMORROW! ONLY HUMILIATION!

DON'T GIVE UP, BUTTER! MAYBE ERIC WILL GET A MEDAL FOR DISPLACING THE MOST AMOUNT OF WATER OUT OF THE POOL!

HI, EVERYONE. I'M SORRY I'VE LET YOU DOWN. I WISH I WAS BRAVE ENOUGH TO GET INTO THE WATER AGAIN... BUT I'M NOT.

DON'T EVEN THINK ABOUT IT, SALMAN! WE DON'T CARE IF WE LOSE SOME SILLY COMPETITION!

THANKS FOR TRYING TO MAKE ME FEEL BETTER, AMAR.

HEY, THAT'S A COOL WATCH!

OH, THANKS! MY DAD GAVE IT TO ME FOR MY BIRTHDAY. IT'S THE BEST PRESENT I'VE EVER GOT!

IT'S GOT A ZILLION FEATURES! AN ALARM CLOCK, A DIGITAL COMPASS, A GAME PLAYER. OH, AND THE DIAL GLOWS DIFFERENT COLOURS IN THE DARK!

WOW!

AWESOME!

IT CAN EVEN READ THE TEMPERATURE AND PREDICT WHETHER IT WILL RAIN OR NOT! CHECK IT OUT!

CAN I SEE IT?

O FORTUNE TELLING WATCH! WILL OUR CRICKET MATCH BE RAINED OUT TODAY AFTERNOON?

55

SALMAN! YOU SWAM LIKE A FISH!

WEREN'T YOU SCARED OF THE WATER?!

NO! I DIDN'T HAVE TIME TO THINK...I JUST DID IT!

YOU SWAM THE LENGTH IN 35 SECONDS, SALMAN! SUPERB! BUT WHY DID YOU JUMP IN WITH ALL YOUR CLOTHES ON?!

IT'S NOT HIS FAULT, SIR! I DROPPED HIS WATCH IN THE POOL AND I...I THINK I'VE RUINED IT!

I'M SO SORRY! I...I'LL BUY YOU A NEW WATCH EVEN IF I HAVE TO GIVE UP MY POCKET MONEY FOR THE NEXT HUNDRED YEARS!

IT'S ALL RIGHT, AMAR. I JUST REMEMBERED! MY WATCH IS WATERPROOF!

WHEW!

I'M NOT SCARED OF THE WATER ANY MORE, THANKS TO YOU, BUTTERFINGERS! AND I'LL WIN OUR SCHOOL SOME MEDALS, JUST WAIT AND SEE!

SWIMMING CHAMPIONSHIP

AND SURE ENOUGH, ON THE DAY OF THE SWIMMING COMPETITION –

WOW! LOOK AT SALMAN GO!

HE'S FASTER THAN A SHARK!

SALMAN

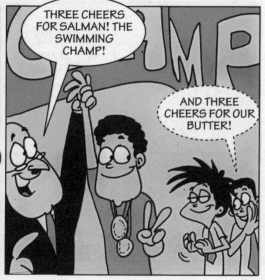

THREE CHEERS FOR SALMAN! THE SWIMMING CHAMP!

AND THREE CHEERS FOR OUR BUTTER!

BUTTERFINGERS AND THE UMBRELLA

Story: Khyrunnisa A.
Script: Anomita Guha
Illustrations and Colouring: Abhijeet Kini

IT WAS A RAINY SATURDAY AND AMAR WAS BORED.

I HATE BEING STUCK AT HOME ALL DAY WITH NOTHING TO DO BECAUSE OF THIS STUPID RAIN!

NOTHING TO DO?! WHY DON'T YOU CLEAN UP THE APPALLING MESS IN YOUR ROOM!

ULP! ME AND MY BIG MOUTH!

!!!!

BAM! BAM!

TRRRNG!

!!!!

WHO'S MAKING THAT RACKET?!

IT HAD BETTER NOT BE ONE OF YOUR IDIOTIC FRIENDS, AMAR!

COLONEL BOGLE!

YES, IT'S ME, AMAR!

RATAN! WHAT'S THE MATTER? YOU SEEM UPSET!

IS EVERYTHING ALL RIGHT?

THERE HAVE BEEN A LOT OF THEFTS NEAR THE STATION RECENTLY. THE POLICE BELIEVE THEM TO BE THE HANDIWORK OF AN EXPERT PICKPOCKET.

THE POLICE ARE ON THE ALERT BUT HE'S ELUDED THEM SO FAR. WE SHOULD REPORT THIS THEFT, RATAN.

DON'T FORGET YOUR UMBRELLA, COLONEL!

SPLUTTER!

AMAR! STOP TRYING TO DROWN COLONEL BOGLE!

SORRY FOR THAT! BUT WHERE'D YOU GET THIS UMBRELLA, SIR? IT'S AMAZING!

IT'S AN ANTIQUE UMBRELLA FROM THAILAND – IT'S QUITE UNIQUE REALLY.

IT IS?

LOOK, THE ORNAMENTAL GLASS AND METAL KNOB COMES OFF…

…LIKE THIS!

WOW!

IT'S AWESOME!

BE CAREFUL WITH THAT!

PHEW! IT'S HEAVIER THAN IT LOOKS! THANK YOU FOR SHOWING IT TO ME, SIR! I WISH MY FRIENDS COULD SEE IT!

WELL, WHY DON'T YOU BORROW IT FOR A DAY OR TWO AND SHOW IT TO THEM? I CAN USE YOUR UMBRELLA TILL THEN!

ER... IT'S KIND OF YOU, RATAN, BUT YOUR UMBRELLA MAY NOT MAKE IT BACK IN ONE PIECE!

NONSENSE! I INSIST!

THANKS SO MUCH, SIR! I'LL TREAT IT LIKE IT'S MADE OF GOLD!

HUMPH! YOU'D BETTER! IF ANYTHING HAPPENS TO THAT UMBRELLA, AMAR, YOU'RE IN BIG TROUBLE!

THE NEXT DAY, AMAR SHOWED OFF THE EXOTIC UMBRELLA TO ALL HIS FRIENDS –

WOW! IT'S REALLY COOL!

CLASSY!

IT'S PROBABLY VERY VALUABLE! GOT TO TAKE GOOD CARE OF IT!

THE UMBRELLA PROVED VERY USEFUL TO AMAR WHEN HE WAS RETURNING HOME IN THE EVENING –

IT'S REALLY POURING!

BOOM!

YIKES!

YEOWW!

WHOOOO!

SWOOSM!

HEY!

STUPID UMBRELLA! I'LL HAVE TO LEAVE IT THERE NOW!

AMAR RETURNED HOME DRENCHED TO THE BONE –

AMAR! WHAT HAPPENED TO YOU?!

YOU LOOK LIKE A SOGGY BISCUIT, YOUNG MAN!

ACHOO! COLONEL BOGLE! I'M SO SORRY...I HAD TO LEAVE YOUR UMBRELLA BEHIND! IT ...IT FLEW OFF INTO A TREE!

WHAT?!

DON'T WORRY, AMAR. YOU CAN GET IT BACK WHEN THE WEATHER CLEARS UP!

NOW DO STOP DRIPPING ALL OVER THE CARPET AND GO DRY YOURSELF!

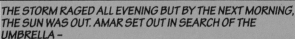

THE STORM RAGED ALL EVENING BUT BY THE NEXT MORNING, THE SUN WAS OUT. AMAR SET OUT IN SEARCH OF THE UMBRELLA –

A LOT OF TREES HAVE FALLEN DOWN! I HOPE THE UMBRELLA'S ALL RIGHT!

THERE IT IS! IT'S MY LUCKY DAY!

OH-OH, THE KNOB IS LOOSE... BETTER UNSCREW IT...

NOW I'LL PULL THIS DARNED UMBRELLA OUT AND...

STOP!

BUTTERFINGERS AND THE ROCK STAR

Story: Khyrunnisa A.
Script: Anomita Guha
Illustrator & Colourist: Abhijeet Kini

UFF !

OW !

I LOVE GOING TO HARIYALI TO SEE GRANDPA... BUT...

...BUT YOU DON'T LOVE THE TRIP ! I KNOW I KNOW !

I WISH PEOPLE WOULD KEEP THEIR ELBOWS TO THEMSELVES !

OUCH ! AND THEIR LUGGAGE TOO !

MAYBE WE SHOULD MOVE TO THE BACK OF THE BUS...THERE'S MORE SPACE THERE.

BUT HOW DO WE GET THERE ?!

JUST PUSH YOUR WAY THROUGH ! WATCH ME !

OOOPS !

HEY !

!!!!

I...I'M SORRY ! I...

WOULD YOU PLEASE GET OFF ME ?!

Y...YES !

YOU OKAY, BUTTER ? YOU LOOK WEIRD !

PEARL JAM

DO YOU KNOW WHO THE GUY I FELL ON WAS ?!

WHO ?!

IT WAS RUSSEL ! THE LEAD SINGER OF THE ROCK BAND, THE HEEBEE JEEBEES !

THEY PLAYED AT OUR SCHOOL ASSEMBLY, REMEMBER?

OH YEAH!

BUT WHAT'S A ROCK STAR LIKE HIM DOING IN A SMALL VILLAGE LIKE HARIYALI?

I DON'T KNOW BUT I'M NOT BRAVE ENOUGH TO ASK HIM RIGHT NOW!

YEAH...HE DIDN'T LOOK VERY HAPPY WHEN YOU SAT ON HIM!

I HOPE HE CALMS DOWN LATER...THEN WE CAN TRY TALKING TO HIM!

AFTER A LONG AND BUMPY RIDE, THE BUS REACHED HARIYALI –

DADA!

BUS ST

KIRAN! HOW I'VE MISSED YOU!

AMAR, GOOD TO SEE YOU TOO!

LIKEWISE, SIR!

DADA, YOU WON'T BELIEVE WHO WAS IN THE BUS WITH US!

BALU WITH HIS PET GOAT?

NOPE! A REAL LIVE ROCK STAR, THAT'S WHO!

LOOK, THERE HE IS! GETTING INTO THAT COOL JEEP!

DO YOU THINK ANYONE ELSE WILL RECOGNISE RUSSEL BESIDES US?

IN THIS VILLAGE? NOT A CHANCE! ONLY YOU KIDS ARE EXCITED ABOUT THESE LONG-HAIRED NOISEMAKERS!

BUT DADA WAS WRONG —

LALU! THAT'S HIM!

YES, BOSS!

WE'RE GOING TO GET RUSSEL IF THAT'S THE LAST THING WE DO!

(GASP!)

KIRAN! DID YOU HEAR?! THOSE TWO MEN KNOW RUSSEL...AND THEY'RE OUT TO GET HIM!

DO YOU THINK HE'S IN DANGER?!

THE NEXT DAY, THEY SET OFF FOR THE TRIPLE STAR FARMHOUSE –

WATCH YOUR STEP, BUTTER! WE CAN'T AFFORD TO GET INTO ANY MORE TROUBLE!

I KNOW! WE'LL JUST WARN RUSSEL AND GO!

HEY, KIDS! HAVE YOU SEEN A LONG-HAIRED FELLOW WITH A BASEBALL CAP AROUND HERE?

(GASP!)

YEAH...HE'S ON THE OTHER SIDE OF THE FARM! PAST THE FLOCK OF GOATS!

THANKS!

MOVE, YOU BLEATING BEASTS!

BAAA! BAAA!

HONK! HONK!

HAH! THAT OUGHT TO DELAY THEM FOR A WHILE!

AT LEAST UNTIL WE FIND RUSSEL OURSELVES!

BUT THAT WAS EASIER SAID THAN DONE –

DRAT! RUSSEL ISN'T IN THE FARMHOUSE!

HE ISN'T EVEN ON THE FARM!

YOU BOYS HAD BETTER EXPLAIN EVERYTHING !

HIS CAP... (SOB !) POOR RUSSEL, POOR HEEBEE JEEBEES !

(SNIFF !)

IT'S TOO TRAGIC ! SO YOUNG...AND GONE SO SOON !

HEY ! THAT'S MY CAP ! THANK GOD YOU FOUND IT !

RUSSEL !

YOU'RE ALIVE !

OF COURSE I AM ! WHY SHOULDN'T I BE ?!

NO...WE THOUGHT THAT YOU...YOU HAD BEEN DROWNED IN THE WELL !

SAY, AREN'T YOU THE SAME KID WHO FELL ON ME...

ER...NEVER MIND THAT ! HOW DID YOUR CAP GET IN THERE ?

A STRONG WIND BLEW IT OFF MY HEAD YESTERDAY AND I THOUGHT I'D LOST IT FOREVER!

I'M THRILLED YOU FOUND THE CAP! I KEEP ALL MY NEWEST SONG LYRICS IN A SECRET COMPARTMENT INSIDE IT!

IT'S A GOOD THING YOUR CAP'S WATER-PROOF!

AND IT'S AN EVEN BETTER THING THAT YOU TWO FOUND IT!

RUSSEL! THERE YOU ARE! WE'VE BEEN LOOKING FOR YOU EVERYWHERE!

WE WOULD HAVE FOUND YOU SOONER IF THESE BOYS HADN'T SENT US ON A WILD GOOSE CHASE!

(ULP!)

WILL YOU CONSIDER SIGNING A CONTRACT WITH US TO PERFORM A SERIES OF CONCERTS? WE'LL MAKE IT WORTH YOUR WHILE!

LET'S DISCUSS IT! NOW THAT I'VE FOUND MY NEW SONGS, THE HEEBEE JEEBEES CAN PUT ON A GREAT SHOW!

AND YOU TWO WILL GET FRONT ROW SEATS TO ALL OF THEM!

WOO HOO!

ROCK ON!